Canada's Food Guide

THE FOOD GUIDE

Are you looking for a simple tool to help you plan your meals and snacks for good health? Try Canada's Food Guide. It is a good place to start.

The Guide is designed to translate the body's nutrient needs into simple food groupings. There are four major food groups, each of which supplies different nutrients to the body. These groups are described on the following pages.

Think of a jigsaw puzzle with four pieces; each piece is essential for completing the puzzle. Two copies of one piece don't make up for a missing part. The same applies to the four food groups. Missing a food group means missing the nutrients supplied by that group. Eating from all four food groups will help you along the good nutrition road.

REMEMBER: CHECK YOUR MAIN MEALS TO BE SURE YOU HAVE SOMETHING FROM EACH OF THE FOUR FOOD GROUPS.

Milk & milk products/2 servings

Each day everyone, including adults and senior citizens, should have two or more servings of milk. The milk may be fresh — whole, 2 per cent, or skim, evaporated, buttermilk, or reconstituted dry non-fat milk. It may be served as a beverage, used on cereals, or in preparing such foods as cream soups, custards or milk puddings. Milk may also be eaten in form of cheese, cottage cheese, yogurt or ice cream.

Foods from the milk group provide calcium which is needed for strong bones and teeth. Milk is also an important source of protein, vitamin A and D, riboflavin, and other nutrients that are needed to maintain good health.

1 serving = 1 cup (8 oz. or 250 ml) milk, yogurt or cottage cheese
1½ ounces (45 g) firm cheese

Meats & alternates/2 servings

Foods in this group include meat, fish, poultry, eggs, nuts, dried beans and peas, peanut butter and cheese. You need two or more servings from this group each day.

Foods from the meat group are an important source of protein which is needed for growth and to repair body tissue. These foods also provide some thiamin, niacin and riboflavin, three vitamins which help the body change food into energy.

With the exception of cheese, these foods also contain iron. An additional iron source, for example, dried fruit, a whole grain or enriched cereal or bread, or a green leafy vegetable must be chosen when cheese is substituted for egg, meat or meat alternate. Iron combines with protein to make hemoglobin, the red substance in the blood which carries oxygen to body cells.

1 serving = 2-3 oz. (60-90 g) lean meat, fish or poultry
2 eggs
1 cup (250 ml) baked beans
4 tablespoons (60 ml) peanut butter
2 oz. (60 g) cheddar, processed or cottage cheese

Bread & Cereals/3 servings

You should eat three or more servings from the breads and cereals group each day.

When purchasing these foods be sure they are either whole grain (eg. rolled oats or whole wheat) or labelled "enriched" (eg. enriched flour, and macaroni, noodles, spaghetti and bread made with enriched flour). Look for brown or converted rice rather than instant — they are more nutritious and less expensive.

Foods from this group provide minerals (especially iron), calories and several B vitamins. Whole wheat and bran are particularly high in these nutrients and also supply roughage.

1 serving = 1 slice bread
1 cup (250 ml) flaked or puffed cereal
¾ cup (200 ml) cooked cereal — oatmeal, noodles, macaroni
1 dinner roll, hamburger or hot dog bun
½ cup (125 ml) cooked brown or converted rice
1 muffin

Fruit & Vegetables/4 servings

You need two servings of fruits and two servings of vegetables daily. They add color, flavor and texture to meals as well as providing nutrients and roughage.

Citrus fruits and juices, tomatoes and tomato juice, strawberries, baked potatoes, broccoli, cauliflower, and cabbage, are valuable sources of vitamin C. Vitamin C is needed for healthy gums and body tissues and helps fight infection. Include one fruit or vegetable rich in vitamin C each day.

Dark green leafy vegetables such as beet greens, Swiss chard, spinach, and deep yellow fruits and vegetables such as carrots, sweet potato, squash, apricots and cantaloupe, are valuable sources of vitamin A. Vitamin A is needed to maintain normal vision and healthy skin. Include one fruit or vegetable rich in vitamin A at least every other day.

1 serving = ½ cup (125 ml) cooked vegetable,
fruit or fruit juice
1 cup (250 ml) raw salad
1 medium size potato, carrot,
tomato, peach, orange, banana

Your daily food should supply all the nutrients your body needs. If you follow the guidelines on the preceding pages, and you choose from a variety of foods each day, you should obtain the essential nutrients in the right amounts.

Other foods

There are other foods which are not included in the daily food guide that are needed to round out meals and meet energy needs. These foods include butter, fortified margarine, and other fats and oils. Vegetable oil (such as safflower, corn or soy) and margarine, are good choices for people who want to lower the cholesterol in their diet. Fats and oils may be used as ingredients in a recipe, or eaten with other foods at the table, but take care not to add too many extra foods or you may find yourself with a weight problem.

Remember:
1. Once you are over 40 your body processes slow down. This means that you don't need as many calories.
2. You may also become less active and not need as many calories for energy.

Did you know?

● Roughage provided by the fibres of cereals, vegetables, and fruits, forms useful bulk which helps prevent constipation. People with denture problems should finely chop or mince these foods. Whole wheat or multi-grain breads have more roughage than white bread. Bran, in muffins (recipe — page 32), in drinks, or eaten as cereal, can be very useful in providing bulk.
● Fluid is needed in large quantities by our bodies. Eight cups of fluid are required each day; more in hot weather or during illness, especially if accompanied by fever or vomiting.
● Liquids can be taken in the form of milk, soup, fruit juices, tea, coffee, or just plain water. Consuming enough fluids helps prevent bladder infection and constipation.

Planning meals

● If you eat one item from each of the four food groups at every meal you should get all the nutrients you need.

Sample Meal Patterns:

Breakfast
    Fruit or juice
    Bread or cereal
    Egg (occasionally)
    Milk or milk products

Luncheon or Supper
    Meat, fish, poultry, egg, dried beans,
      cheese* or meat alternates
    Fruit or vegetable

    Bread or cereal
    Milk or milk product

Dinner
    Meat, fish, poultry, egg, dried beans,
      cheese* or meat alternates
    Fruit or vegetable
    Bread or cereal
    Milk or milk product

*An additional iron source must be chosen when cheese is substituted for meat, eg. dried fruit, whole grain or enriched bread or cereal, or, a leafy green vegetable.

● Try to plan menus for a week at a time.

● Divide the foods fairly evenly among meals. If one meal must be heartier, mid-day is usually best, allowing for more complete digestion before bedtime.

● While three meals a day are usual, many people prefer to eat four or more lighter meals a day. If serving sizes are small, use more servings from each group every day. Just be careful to avoid overeating as little meals can grow into big ones very easily.

● Get into the habit of eating at regular times — your body might not like "surpirses".

● Plan for a variety of color, flavor and texture to add interest to meals.

● Plan "leftovers" for another meal.

Be kind to your heart

Consider your heart when planning meals and snacks. Researchers have found that eating diets high in fat, sugar and salt and low in "fibre foods" is linked to a high risk of heart disease. Some of the changes you may choose to make in your present lifestyle are:

1. Use Canada's Food Guide everyday for your meal planning.
2. Cut down on fat as much as possible.
   - Trim off visible fat from your meat.
   - Eat fish or poultry more often than red meats.
   - Try skim milk or lowfat dairy products.
   - Cook without added fat, ie. broiling, baking, steaming or poaching.
3. Cut down on sugars including honey, jams, jellies, candies, soft drinks, sweet pastries and desserts.
4. Watch the salt!
   - Taste before you add salt to your foods.
   - Eat fewer salty foods such as potato chips, pretzels, luncheon meats, weiners and pickles.

Serving Meals

Eating alone does not have to be dull. Keep some of the atmosphere that went with an enjoyable family dinner.

Make a concentrated effort to relax, eat slowly, and enjoy your food. Choose a small table, tea tray, or lap tray so you can vary your eating spots. Sit near a window or go outside on the porch. Take your lunch to the park for a picnic. Invite a friend to join you for a meal — you'll both enjoy it.

Reading, listening to music, or watching television while eating, can make meal times one of the high spots of the day.

Remember: the better the food looks, the better it tastes. Treat yourself occasionally by using your fine china and cutlery; you'll be surprised how much you enjoy the meal — even if you are by yourself.

Meals away from home

Meals out can be a real treat, especially if enjoyed with a friend. Just remember to watch that you achieve a balanced diet.

Daily specials are frequently excellent value if they aren't too high in carbohydrates (starches) and fats.

Social groups often plan suppers prepared by their members. This food is usually very good and inexpensive. Investigate the clubs and churches in your area. It is often a good chance to make new friends and enjoy a delicious meal.

If you do go to a luncheon or banquet, some of the following tips may help you control your fat and sugar intake:

● Remove gravy from meat. Trim the fat. Remove coatings from breaded fried foods.

● Ask for salad dressing on the side. Use only a small amount of butter on your roll (saves 50 calories).

● At a buffet, choose the low fat items eg. roast meats, green salads and raw vegetables.

Using simple equipment

The recipes that follow, and many others, can be prepared with a minimum of equipment.

If you don't have a range you can cook with a hotplate. Many of the recipes in this booklet are for "top-of-the-stove" cooking.

A cast-iron fry pan or skillet can be used both on the top of the stove or as a roast pan in the oven. Saucepans with metal or heat-resistant handles can also be used in the oven or on direct heat. Custard cups can double for muffin or cupcake tins.

Even with limited equipment you can cook tasty meals that are well balanced and varied.

Shopping & storing foods

● If shopping is difficult it might be wise to have groceries delivered, even if you have to pay for this service.
● Check foods on hand before you shop. Make a list of foods you need for the meals you've planned.
● Buy foods in season for best quality; watch for "specials".
● Do not buy more food than you can store properly.
● Keep in mind the amount and kinds of food storage space you have.
● Large amounts of food are often cheaper, but if they spoil before you use them, you won't be saving any money.
● Don't shop when you are hungry.
● Read labels. Contents are always listed in descending order by quantity.

Each section in this booklet has additional tips on what to look for when buying and storing a particular food.

Emergency shelf

It is useful to have a small supply of emergency food available in case you are unable to get out due to illness, bad weather or an emergency.

The following list of foods could be included on your shelf. Be sure to use these items from time to time and to replace them with fresh ones:

    Cans of meat or fish
    Dried or canned milk
    Cans of fruit and vegetables
    Cans of soup
    Whole wheat crackers
    Tea or coffee
    Enriched noodles

Cheese & milk

Milk and milk products are an excellent source of protein, riboflavin, vitamins A and D, and calcium.

Buying

- To stretch your milk budget mix fresh milk with reconstituted skim milk powder for drinking.
- Use reconstituted dried milk for cooking.
- Evaporated milk is a good buy if storage facilities are inadequate.
- Mild cheddar cheese is usually less expensive per pound than processed cheese slices. Store brands are usually cheaper than brand names.
- Use cottage cheese often because there is no waste and no preparation required. Uncreamed or 2 per cent is less expensive and lower in calories.
- If you are watching calories or cholesterol, skim milk, skim milk cheese and ice milk are your best choices.

Storage

- Refrigerated fresh milk should be used within a week.
- Unrefrigerated milk should be used within one day. Buy only as much as you can use in a day if storage space is limited.
- Evaporated milk can be stored for months unopened. Once opened, use within three or four days.
- Skim milk powder can be kept for months in a cool dry place.
- Cheese is best kept cool to preserve its goodness. Once the package is opened use as soon as possible or store in a plastic wrap.
- Hard cheese may be stored as long as three months but soft cheese should be eaten within a week.
- Cottage cheese can only be stored a few days.

HOMEMADE YOGURT

Serves 2

2 cups 2% skim, or whole milk
1½ tsp. yogurt, unflavoured
¼ cup skim milk powder

Mix milk and milk powder in heavy saucepan (if milk powder does not completely dissolve, strain out lumps). Bring to a boil, stirring constantly. Cool to lukewarm. Stir in yogurt until smooth. Pour mixture into a warmed thermos. Leave 5-6 hours or overnight. Refrigerate when mixture is consistency of thick cream.

If you don't have a thermos put mixture in clean jars and wrap in heating pad at lowest setting.

To make fruit yogurt add fruit (berries, sliced peaches, apple sauce, etc.) a few hours or the night before you plan to eat it to blend the flavors.

Suggestion for completing meal — rye toast spread with peanut butter, apple (if plain yogurt is used).

CHEESE SOUFFLE

180 C (350 F)
Serves 1

1/3 cup shredded cheddar cheese
1 egg, separated
½ cup soft bread crumbs
½ cup scalded milk

Mix together cheese, egg yolk, bread crumbs, and milk. Beat egg white until stiff and fold into other mixture. Turn into casserole and sprinkle with 1 tablespoon shredded cheese. Bake at 350°F for 15-20 minutes until knife inserted comes out clean. Serve immediately.

Suggestion for completing meal — tangy fruit salad (p. 15)

MACARONI AND CHEESE

230 C (450 F)
Serves 2

½ cup macaroni
½ cup medium cheese sauce (see below)
bread crumbs

Cook macaroni until tender. Drain and rinse with cold water. Prepare cheese sauce (see p. 8) and add macaroni. If an oven is available, turn mixture into a baking dish, top with bread crumbs, brown in a hot oven, and serve. If an oven is not available, heat mixture until warmed through and serve immediately.

Suggestion for completing meal — sausages and sliced tomato.

CHEESE SAUCE

½ cup medium white sauce (see below) dash of cayenne
½ tsp. dry mustard 1/3 - ½ cup grated cheddar cheese

Prepare medium white sauce, adding ½ tsp. dry mustard and dash of cayenne with seasonings. Add cheddar cheese at end of cooking. Stir until cheese is melted. Serve with vegetables or macaroni.

BASIC WHITE SAUCE (MEDIUM)   Serves 1

1 tbsp. butter dash of salt
1 tbsp. flour dash of pepper
¼ cup skim milk powder ½ cup water

Melt butter, blend in flour, seasonings and skim milk powder. Gradually add water. Stir and cook until smooth and thick. Makes about ½ cup.

BASIC PUDDING MIX

2/3 cup cornstarch ¾ tsp. salt
1 cup sugar 4 cups skim milk powder

Mix ingredients and sift 3 times. Store in tightly covered container. Makes 5 cups of mix.

Variations:

1. VANILLA PUDDING   Serves 1

   1/3 cup basic pudding mix 2 tsp. butter
   ½ cup water ½ tsp. vanilla

To basic pudding mix add ½ cup water. Stir and cook in double boiler until thick (about 10 minutes). Stir in 2 tsp. butter. Cool slightly and add vanilla.

2. CHOCOLATE PUDDING   Serves 1

   1/3 cup basic pudding mix 1 tbsp. cocoa

To basic pudding mix add 1 tbsp. cocoa and make as Vanilla Pudding.

3. COCONUT PUDDING   Serves 1

   1/3 cup basic pudding mix 1-2 tbsp. coconut

To basic pudding mix add 1-2 tbsp. coconut and make as Vanilla Pudding. For special occasions: after pudding is cooked, alternate layers of pudding and fruit in tall clear glasses.

4. PIE FILLING   Makes 1-9 inch pie

Any of the above puddings may be used as a pie filling by increasing the amount of ingredients used and adding 2 beaten egg yolks.

    1 cup basic pudding mix   3 times flavouring used in pudding recipe
    1½ cups water   2 beaten egg yolks

Prepare as Vanilla Pudding. When thick, gradually add a little hot mixture to egg yolks. Return to remaining hot mixture and cook 1-2 minutes. Fills 1 baked 9-inch pie shell.

Suggestion for completing meal — meat sandwich on whole wheat bread and a green salad.

CREAM OF CHICKEN SOUP   Serves 2

    1½ cups liquid from cooking vegetables   ½ cup chopped cooked chicken
    ¾ cup skim milk powder   ½ cup cooked celery
    1½ tbsp. flour   1 tbsp. cooked onion
    ½ tsp. salt   1/8 tsp. thyme

Place vegetable water in saucepan. Combine skim milk powder, flour and salt. Sprinkle this mixture over the liquid and beat it until mixed and smooth. Cook at medium heat until mixture thickens. Add chicken, celery, onion and thyme, and continue cooking at low heat.

Suggestion for completing meal — whole wheat crackers and peaches.

CHEESE STRAWS   230 C (450 F)
                                                                                        Serves 2

    3 tbsp. whole wheat flour   pinch of salt
    1 tbsp. enriched white flour   ¾ cup finely grated cheese
    1 tsp. wheat germ   2 tsp. margarine
    1/8 tsp. baking powder

Sift all dry ingredients together. Cut in margarine and cheese. Add water to moisten and make into a ball. Roll out 1/8 inch thick and cut in sticks. Bake for 5-8 minutes.

Suggestion for completing snack — a glass of tomato juice.

BROILED SUPER SANDWICH   Serves 1

    1 slice cheese   tomato slices
    1 slice bread, toasted   cooked bacon

Place a slice of cheese on toast, broil until cheese begins to melt. Add sliced tomato and lots of cooked bacon. Broil until tomato is hot. Serve immediately.

A balanced meal.

CHEESE MUFFINS

200 C (400 F)
Makes 6 muffins

1 cup flour
2 tsp. baking powder
¼ tsp. salt
2 tbsp. sugar

½ cup grated leftover cheddar cheese
1 egg
½ cup milk
1 tbsp. oil

Sift dry ingredients. Add grated cheese. Combine egg, milk and oil and add all liquids to dry ingredients at once. Stir lightly only until moistened. Spoon into oiled muffin tins, 2/3 full. Bake 20 to 25 minutes until tops of muffins are golden brown.

Suggestion for completing meal — Shepherd's pie (p. 56).

APPLE BREAD PUDDING

180 C (350 F)
Serves 2

2 slices cubed whole wheat bread
1 cup milk
1 slightly beaten egg
1½ tbsp. light molasses

½ cup peeled, diced apples
1 tbsp. raisins
pinch of salt
pinch of nutmeg

Soak bread cubes in milk. Add egg, molasses, apples, raisins, salt and nutmeg. Mix and place in small greased casserole and bake for 45 minutes or until set.

Suggestion for completing meal — chef salad containing leftover roast beef, cubes of cheese, lettuce, grated carrot and sliced tomatoes.

BROCCOLI "QUICHE"

180 C (350 F)

Crust:

½ cup whole wheat flour
1 tsp. baking powder
pinch of salt
¼ cup margarine
2 tbsp. skim milk

Filling:

½ cup cooked, diced broccoli
¼ cup **dry** cottage cheese
1/3 cup grated Swiss or cheddar
1 lightly beaten egg
1/3 cup skim milk
2 tbsp. chopped chives or green onion
1 tbsp. sesame seeds (optional)

Lightly oil a small oven-proof casserole. Combine whole wheat flour, baking powder, and salt. Using a pastry blender or a fork mix the margarine in until the mixture resembles coarse crumbs. Add milk. Using the back of a spoon, spread and press the mixture against the bottom and sides of the casserole dish. Place broccoli on top of the crust. Combine cottage cheese, milk, cheddar cheese, egg and chopped onion and pour over broccoli. Sprinkle with sesame seeds. Bake in preheated 350°F oven for 45 minutes or until set.

A complete meal.

COTTAGE STUFFED TOMATO
Serves 1

2 tbsp. diced celery
1 tbsp. snipped chives
pinch of fine herbs

½ cup cottage cheese (2%)
1 medium tomato
parsley

Combine first four ingredients. Turn tomato stem side down. Cut not quite through into six equal wedges. Spread open slightly and fill with cottage cheese mixture.

Suggestion for completing meal — dill bread and sardines. (p. 35)

WELSH RAREBIT
Serves 2

1 tbsp. butter
1 tbsp. flour
¼ tsp. dry mustard
¾ cup milk (skim or 2%)

¾ cup grated sharp cheddar cheese
dash of worcestershire sauce
pinch of salt, optional

Melt butter in top of double boiler over boiling water, or over low heat. Combine flour and dry mustard and add to butter. Stir to blend. Very gradually stir in milk. Cook stirring constantly, until smoothly thickened. Add grated cheese, stir until melted. Add seasonings. Serve over whole wheat toast. Sprinkle with paprika.

Suggestion for completing meal — sliced tomato, spear of broccoli and sliced chicken.

CORN CHOWDER
Serves 2

1 medium potato, cubed
¼ cup chopped onion
1 can creamed corn (14 oz.)

1 cup milk
salt and pepper (to taste)

Cook potato and onion until tender in a small amount of water. Do not drain. Add milk and corn. Heat, season and serve.

Suggestion for completing meal — whole wheat crackers and liver sausage.

Fruit & vegetables

Choosing a variety of fruits and vegetables will compliment your meal by adding color, flavor, texture, roughage and additional food value, especially vitamins A and C.

Vegetables particularly should be "tender-crisp"— cooked enough to be done but not mushy. This is particularly important for green vegetables. Once they have turned a greenish-yellow color they are overcooked.

Buying

● Buying fresh fruits and vegetables when in season.
— in winter choose oranges, grapefruit, bananas and root vegetables (potato, turnips, onions and carrots).
— in summer most salad vegetables including tomatoes are a good buy. Corn and beans are also abundant. Summer fruits include peaches, cherries, melons and a variety of berries.
— in fall buy cabbage, broccoli, beets, cauliflower and squash as well as apples, pears, plums and grapes.
— in spring buy strawberries, rhubarb, lettuce, beet greens and spinach.

● When fresh fruit and vegetables are not in season, frozen or canned products, especially "store" brands, are generally more economical.

● Fruits and vegetables make nutritious and inexpensive snacks that are easy on the waistline.

● Fancy, choice and standard grades of canned fruits and vegetables are equally nutritious but vary in appearance (size, firmness, color) and price. Standard grade, when available, is generally the lowest priced.

● Specially packaged fruit or vegetable products (such as foil-wrapped potatoes or peas in butter sauce) are seldom economical buys.

● As a rule of thumb the smallest vegetables (eg. baby peas, new potatoes) and the largest fruits are the choicest and also the most expensive.

Storage

● Store asparagus, green beans, greens, brussels sprouts, cabbage and cauliflower in a plastic bag in refrigerator.
● Store egg plant, green peppers, mushrooms and tomatoes uncovered in refrigerator.
● Store potatoes, onions, squash, turnips, beets and carrots in a cool, dry, airy place or in the refrigerator. They will keep for several weeks.
● Fresh corn, peas and greens should be used as soon as possible (1-2 days).

SAUCY VEGETABLES* (A Good Vitamin A Recipe) — Serves 1

1 small potato, diced
1 small carrot, sliced
¼ cup frozen or canned peas
1/3 can cream of mushroom soup
1 tbsp. cheddar cheese, grated
½ tbsp. powdered skim milk

Cook vegetables until just tender. Drain vegetables (keep water the vegetables were cooked in for soup or gravy). Mix soup, cheese and milk together in saucepan. Heat on low until cheese melts. Add vegetables to sauce, leave on heat until vegetables are heated thoroughly.

Suggestion for completing meal — a slice of meat loaf, whole wheat roll and milk.

*Top of the Stove Recipe

BAKED POTATO (A Good Vitamin C Recipe) — 200 C (400 F)

Baking is the very best way to serve potatoes. Most of the vitamin C is saved if they are baked. Do not peel; scrub the potatoes, prick with a fork and bake in hot oven (400°F) for about 1 hour. Serve at once with butter or margarine, or onions sprinkled on top. Easy and elegant.

Suggestion for completing meal — Simple Simon Chicken (p. 27) with strawberries and ice milk for dessert.

FRESH FRUIT SALAD

For a fresh fruit salad choose any combination of fresh fruits, cut into small pieces, and cover with unsweetened orange juice to prevent browning. Serve chilled. It's easy and creative.

CINNAMON PEARS

Serves 1

1 fresh pear
2 tsp. melted butter or margarine
¼ tsp. sugar
¼ tsp. cinnamon

Wash pear but do not peel. Cut pear in half lengthwise and remove centre core. Place cut side up on pie plate or aluminum foil, brush with melted butter or margarine. Mix cinnamon and sugar together. Sprinkle sugar and cinnamon mixture over pears. Place under the broiler and broil approximately 8 minutes. Serve hot or cold.

Suggestion for completing meal — cream of tomato soup and egg salad sandwich.

AN EASY VEGETABLE IDEA

Cabbage has more vitamin C than lettuce and is much less expensive. Serve it often as coleslaw.

GINGER CARROTS

180 C (350 F)
Serves 1

½ cup coarsely chopped peeled carrots
1 tsp. lemon juice
1 tbsp. water
1/8 tsp. of ginger
pinch of salt
pinch of pepper
1 tbsp. margarine

Place the carrots in a small greased casserole. Combine lemon juice, water and seasoning and pour over carrots. Dot with margarine. Cover and place in oven for 35 minutes or until the carrots are tender crisp.

Suggestion for completing meal — Breaded fish (p. 23), baked brown rice (p. 49), and yogurt (p. 7).

CARROTS IN CASSEROLE

190 C (375 F)
Serves 1

1 large carrot
1 tsp. butter or margarine
dash of salt and pepper
1-2 tbsp. water

Coarsely chop carrot and place in greased casserole. Dot with butter or margarine and season with salt and pepper to taste. Add a tablespoon or two of water. Cover and bake until tender (35 minutes).

Try this same method with turnip, parsnip, beets or onions.

Suggestion for completing meal — salmon loaf (p. 24) and chocolate pudding (p. 8).

BERT'S SPECIAL SALAD
Serves 1

¼ cup chopped raw zucchini
1 small tomato (in wedges)
a few small spinach leaves
¼ cup alfalfa sprouts
1½ cups cheese (cubed)
1 tbsp. oil and vinegar salad dressing

Toss salad ingredients lightly with salad dressing.

Suggestion for completing meal — a tuna sandwich on rye bread.

TROPICAL FRUIT SMOOTHIE
Serves 1

1 medium banana*
1½ cups unsweetened pineapple juice*
½ cup natural yogurt

Mash banana well. Place in a jar or small plastic container with a tight fitting lid. Add juice and yogurt. Blend well with an egg beater or put lid on container and "shake". Serve over ice cubes for a refreshing nutritious drink.

*Use any combination of fruit and fruit juice and create your own fruit smoothies.

BAKED APPLE
200 C (400 F)
Serves 1

1 apple
1 tsp. butter or margarine
1 tbsp. brown sugar
¼ tsp. cinnamon
2 tbsp. water

Wash and core the apple. Stuff the apple with a mixture of 1 tsp. butter or margarine, 1 tbsp. brown sugar and ¼ tsp. cinnamon. Place apple in pan and add 2 tbsp. water. Bake ½ hour.

This is a handy dessert if you are baking a main course.

Suggestion for completing meal — tuna noodle casserole (p. 25).

TANGY FRUIT SALAD
Serves 1

1 small orange or ½ cup of berries
½ small banana, sliced
cinnamon
1 tbsp. yogurt
1 tbsp. orange juice

If using orange, peel, slice and quarter slices. Combine in bowl with banana. Combine orange juice and yogurt. Pour over fruit and toss lightly. Sprinkle with cinnamon.

Suggestion for completing meal — bran muffin (p. 32), cottage cheese, and walnuts.

RATATOUILLE
Serves 1

1 small zucchini, sliced OR
1 cup cubed yellow squash
2 tsp. vegetable oil
½ cup canned tomatoes
salt and pepper to taste

2 tbsp. chopped onion
¼ tsp. fine herbs
1 tsp. snipped parsley
1 tsp. grated cheese, (optional)

Measure oil into saucepan with tight-fitting lid. Add zucchini and onion and saute a few minutes. Add tomato and seasonings. Cover and simmer gently about 20 minutes or until vegetables are cooked. Sprinkle with parsley and cheese before serving.

Suggestion for completing meal – whole wheat roll and a piece of cheese.

STIR-FRY VEGETABLES
Serves 1

2 teaspoons oil
1 small carrot, sliced thinly
½ cup green beans, sliced diagonally
few drops of lemon juice

½ stalk celery, sliced diagonally
  and thinly
pinch of salt and pepper

Heat oil in heavy skillet on high heat. Add carrots and beans, stir vegetables constantly for a minute or two. Add celery and two to three tablespoons of water, cover and **steam** a few minutes, until vegetables are tender-crisp. Season with salt, pepper and lemon juice.

Suggestion for completing meal – broiled fish, brown rice and milk.

Other combination: broccoli, onion, celery
   cauliflower, onion, mushrooms
   zucchini and fresh tomato wedges
   asparagus and sliced mushrooms

VEGETABLE BEEF CASSEROLE
180 C (350 F)
Serves 1

3 oz. ground beef
vegetable oil
2 tbsp. finely chopped onion
¼ cup canned tomatoes
pinch of salt and pepper or fine herbs

1 tbsp. flour
½ cup steamed, mashed squash
grated parmesan cheese or dry
   bread crumbs

Brown beef in small frypan using just enough oil to coat the bottom of pan. Drain off excess fat. Add onion and cook a few minutes longer. Sprinkle flour over top and stir to mix. Stir in canned tomatoes and simmer a few minutes to thicken. Place meat mixture in small casserole. Top with mashed squash, sprinkle with cheese or bread crumbs. Bake in 350°F oven for 25 minutes or until heated through.

Suggestion for completing meal – whole wheat roll and cheese (used in the recipe or on the side).

Vegetable protein

Vegetable proteins include a variety of legumes, dried peas, dried beans and nuts. Vegetable proteins are a good substitute for meat and much less expensive.

Pea soup, baked beans, and peanut butter sandwiches are just a few of the favourites containing vegetable protein.

Buying

- Dried peas and beans are much less expensive than canned.
- Large quantities of dried legumes are usually less expensive.

Storing

- Peanut butter keeps well after opening.
- Store dried peas and beans in a cool place.

Basic Cooking for Legumes

TYPE OF LEGUME	AMOUNT OF LEGUME	AMOUNT OF WATER	COOKING TIME (simmering gently on top of stove)	YIELD
Lentils or split peas (no soaking needed)	1/3 cup	1 cup	45 mins.	1 cup
Kidney and navy (small white) beans — soak overnight and add ½ teaspoon salt	½ cup	1½ cups*	2 hours	1¼ cups
Small lima beans — soak overnight and add ½ teaspoon salt	½ cup	1½ cups*	1 hour	1 cup
Soy beans — soak overnight and add ½ teaspoon salt	½ cup	2 cups*	3 hours	1¼ cups

*Use soaking water in cooking.

SPLIT PEA SOUP

Serves 2

½ cup uncooked dry split peas (or lentils)
1 small onion, chopped
1 small stalk of celery with leaves, chopped
1 tbsp. chopped carrots
2 cups water
½ tsp. salt
1 tbsp. butter or margarine
¼ tsp. thyme

Wash and drain split peas or lentils. Put all ingredients in a pan. Heat to boiling. Cover and boil gently about 30 minutes until split peas or lentils are tender.

Note: Add pieces of canned luncheon meat, frankfurters or cooked ham before serving the soup, if desired.

Suggestion for completing meal — bran muffin, banana and yogurt.

SAVORY BEAN/OAT PATTIES　　　　　　　　　　　　　　　　　　　　　　　　　　　Serves 2

　　　　1/3 cup rolled oats　　　　　　　　1 tbsp. soya sauce
　　　　2 tbsp. onion, chopped　　　　　　salt and pepper to taste
　　　　½ stalk celery, chopped　　　　　　½ cup garbanzo beans (pre-cooked or canned)
　　　　¼ tsp. sage　　　　　　　　　　　　¼ cup liquid from beans

Mash beans thoroughly with a fork and stir in liquid and rolled oats. Add celery, onion, sage, soya sauce, salt and pepper. Mix well. Let mixture stand for a few minutes to allow oats to absorb the moisture. Shape mixture into 2 medium-size patties. Cook at low temperature in a lightly oiled skillet, about 10 minutes each side. Serve with tomato sauce. Make easy tomato sauce by heating 2/3 cup of undiluted tomato soup.

Suggestion for completing meal — broccoli, Irish bran bread (p. 34) and baked cottage cheese custard (p. 42).

BAKED BEANS　　　　　　　　　　　　　　　　　　　　　　　　　　　　　150 C (300 F)
　　Serves 1

　　　　1/3 cup dry navy beans　　　　　　¼ tsp. salt
　　　　2 tbsp. chopped onions　　　　　　¼ tsp. vinegar
　　　　1 tbsp. molasses　　　　　　　　　1 tsp. Worcestershire sauce (optional)
　　　　1 tbsp. catsup　　　　　　　　　　1 1/3 cups water
　　　　1 tsp. dry mustard　　　　　　　　1 slice of bacon, uncooked and chopped
　　　　　　　　　　　　　　　　　　　　　　　(optional)

Cover beans with 1 1/3 cup water and soak overnight. Place beans and water on stove and bring to a boil, reduce heat and simmer gently until the beans are soft, about 40 minutes. Drain beans, reserving liquid. Add onion, catsup, dry mustard, salt, vinegar, Worcestershire sauce and ¼ cup of reserved liquid from beans. Place in a small greased casserole, top with chopped bacon and bake covered for 2½ hours at 300°. Check periodically and add more water from the beans if baked beans become dry.

Suggestion for completing meal — corn bread, coleslaw and milk.

LENTIL AND RICE CASSEROLE　　　　　　　　　　　　　　　　　　　　　　180 C (350 F)
　　Serves 2

　　　　1/3 cup lentils　　　　　　　　　　2 tbsp. chopped onions
　　　　¼ cup rice, uncooked　　　　　　　1 tbsp. vegetable oil
　　　　salt and pepper to taste　　　　　1¼ cups liquid (bouillon, tomato juice,
　　　　　　　　　　　　　　　　　　　　　　　soup stock)

Heat oil in small skillet and saute the onion until lightly browned. Stir in lentils and rice, continue stirring until rice and lentils are well coated with oil. Season with salt and pepper and fry gently for about one minute. Put mixture in small casserole, pour liquid over rice. Bake covered for 45 minutes, or until all the liquid is absorbed.

Suggestion for completing meal — tossed salad and baked custard.

TOMATO LENTIL SOUP
Serves 2

1/3 cup lentils
2 tbsp. chopped onion
2 tbsp. brown rice

1½ cups of water
1 (10 oz.) can tomato soup
1 soup can of water

Measure lentils, rice, onion, and 1½ cups water into saucepan. Bring to boil, cover and simmer until beans and rice are cooked, about 45 minutes. Add tomato soup and one soup can of water. Heat and serve.

Suggestion for completing meal — celery and carrot stick, whole wheat crackers, and cheese.

BARLEY VEGETABLE PILAF
190 C (375 F)
Serves 2

¼ cup pearl barley
2 tsp. chopped onion
1 tsp. margarine

½ tsp. bouillon powder OR ½ bouillon cube
 (chicken or beef)
¼ cup peas (fresh or frozen)
¾ cup liquid (water or vegetable stock)

Slightly brown barley and onion in margarine. Turn into small casserole. Add peas. Heat liquid, add bouillon and stir to dissolve. Pour over ingredients in casserole and stir to mix. Cover and bake in 375°F oven, one hour.

Suggestion for completing meal — chicken mushroom casserole (p. 28), baked apple, and a glass of milk.

Fish & seafood

Fish is an excellent alternate for meat. It is lower in cost than most red meat, and generally contains fewer calories and less fat.

Buying

● Fish fillets are usually the best buy frozen or fresh.
● Frozen fish that has been pre-breaded, precooked, or mixed with other ingredients such as potato, is a convenient but expensive buy.
● Several varieties of canned fish are good buys, particularly mackerel and chicken haddie.
● Canned tuna is generally a good buy, especially if on sale.
● There is little difference in food value of the colors of canned salmon. Therefore, if appearance does not matter, buy the cheapest brand.
● A can of sardines is often a good buy. Cans containing 7-8 larger fish are much less expensive than the ones containing many small fish. There isn't any nutritive difference.

Storage

● Fresh or frozen fish must be stored frozen as it spoils quickly.
● Fish can only be kept in a "top of the fridge" freezer for about a week as the quality deteriorates rapidly.
● Use fish before 3 months even when stored in a regular freezer.
● Canned fish can be stored indefinitely if unopened.
● Opened canned fish should be stored in the refrigerator in a covered container. Use within a day or two.

*The Secret for Cooked Fish

1. Do not overcook. Overcooking toughens and dries out the flesh.
2. Cook fish at high temperature for a short period of time:

Oven   400-500°F (200°C-260°C)
Pan frying } hot but not smoking
Pan broiling
Oven broiling   four inches from heat

3. Cook fresh fish 10 minutes for every inch of thickness. Cook frozen fish 20 minutes for every inch of thickness. Measure with a ruler at the thickest part. Don't rely on a guess!
4. Frozen fish stays more moist when cooked in its frozen state.
5. Fish is cooked when:
— the juices are milky
— the flesh is easily pierced with a fork and will easily separate into flakes
— the flesh takes on a whitish tinge

BAKED FISH WITH HERBS

230 C (450 F)
Serves 1

1 fish fillet (approx. 3 oz.)
milk
dry bread crumbs or cornmeal
¼-½ tsp. your favourite herbs
lemon slices

Soak fish fillet in milk for 3 minutes. Drain well and roll in dry bread crumbs or cornmeal. Place on a piece of heavy duty aluminum foil. Lightly sprinkle with herbs and add lemon slices. Seal the foil. Place on a cookie sheet and bake. Length of baking time depends on thickness of fish — 10 minutes per inch of thickness. Twice that time if the fish is frozen.

Suggestion for completing meal — vegetable rice pilaf (p. 33), coconut pudding (p. 8).

SALMON FRENCH TOAST

Serves 2

3¾ oz. tin of salmon
   (tuna could be used)
1½ tbsp. mayonnaise
1 tbsp. chopped onion
1 tbsp. chopped parsley (optional)
¼ tsp. salt
dash of pepper

4 slices of enriched white or
   whole wheat bread
1 egg well beaten
½ cup liquid (salmon juice plus water
   to make ½ cup)
2 tbsp. skim milk powder

Drain salmon and save the juice. Flake the salmon and crush the bones. Mix salmon with mayonnaise, parsley, onion and seasonings. Spread on two slices of bread and top with the other two. Combine beaten egg, salmon liquid and skim milk powder in a shallow dish. Dip sandwiches in this mixture and brown both sides in hot oiled frying pan.

Suggestion for completing meal — green salad and glass of milk.

BREADED FISH FILLETS

Serves 1

1 small fish fillet
¼ cup milk
2 tbsp. dry bread crumbs
1 tbsp. oil

Soak fish fillets in milk containing dash of salt and pepper for 3 minutes. Drain and roll in dry bread crumbs. Preheat oil in skillet and fry fillet until all flesh flakes easily and becomes opaque.

Suggestion for completing meal — saucy vegetables (p. 13), whole wheat bread.

SAUCY FISH AND PEAS

Serves 1

1½ tsp. margarine
1½ tsp. flour
dash of salt and pepper
¼ cup powdered skim milk
½ cup canned peas, drained
½ cup liquid from drained peas
3 oz. canned tuna or other cooked fish

Using margarine, flour, salt and pepper, skim milk powder and liquid from can of peas, make a medium white sauce (see page 8). Heat the sauce and add peas and tuna. Serve over noodles, rice or toast.

A complete meal.

FISH FOIL DINNER

200 C (400 F)
Serves 1

1/3 package frozen fish fillets
1 tsp. butter or margarine
2 tsp. lemon juice
1/8 tsp. salt
dash of pepper
1 tbsp. chopped onion
1 small potato
1 small carrot
1 thick slice tomato
1 heaping tsp. mayonnaise
1 oz. grated cheddar cheese

Tear off a piece of heavy foil 12" x 16" with shiny side of the foil to the inside, spread 1 tsp. butter or margarine around the centre. Place the fillet in the foil. Season with salt, pepper and lemon juice. Place slice of tomato on the fish and add mayonnaise. Slice the potato and carrot very thin, arrange over and around the fish (for variety use green beans and mushrooms) Add the chopped onion. Top all with cheese.

Closing the package is important to keep steam and juices from escaping. Bring the two longest sides together and fold over at least twice. Then flatten the ends and fold them toward the centre at least twice.

Place foil package on a pan and bake at 400°F for 45 minutes.

Note: Cut through frozen fillets with a strong serrated knife or better still ask the butcher to saw through the fish for you.

Suggestion for completing meal — sour milk muffin (p. 57).

SEAFARER'S CASSEROLE

160 C (325 F)
Serves 2

1 (7¾ oz.) can pink salmon
2 eggs
¼ tsp. dry mustard
pinch of salt and pepper

3 tbsp. skim milk powder
1 tbsp. chopped chives OR
½ tsp. onion flakes
paprika

Drain salmon, reserving juice. Add water to juice to measure ½ cup. Stir in 3 tablespoons skim milk powder. Set aside. Mash salmon including bones. Beat eggs lightly with fork. Stir in milk mixture, salmon, mustard, salt, and pepper. Pour into two individual greased casseroles. Sprinkle with paprika. Bake at 325°F for 25 minutes or until a knife inserted just off centre comes out clean.

Suggestions for completing meal — green bean salad with oil and vinegar dressing and baking powder biscuits.

SALMON LOAF

180 C (350 F)
Serves 2

1 (7¾ oz.) can salmon
1 egg
salt and pepper
½ cup soft bread crumbs

¼ cup chopped celery
¼ cup chopped onion
dash of Worcestershire sauce

Mash can of salmon, liquid, bones and all in a bowl. Add remaining ingredients and blend well. Put into a lightly greased casserole or loaf pan. Bake 40-45 minutes or until top is browned.

Suggestion for completing meal — broccoli and glass of milk.

HEARTY FISH CHOWDER

Serves 2

1/3 pound of fish fillets
2 tbsp. chopped celery
1 small potato, diced
¾ cup boiling water or vegetable stock
½ cup skim milk

2 tsp. margarine
2 tbsp. chopped onion
1 small carrot, sliced
¼ tsp. salt and pepper

Cut fillet into bite-sized pieces. Melt margarine in saucepan and cook onion and celery until tender. Add potatoes, carrots, water, salt, and pepper. Cover and simmer 10 to 15 minutes until vegetables are tender. Add fish and cook 10 minutes longer. Add milk, reheat but do not boil.

Suggestion for completing meal — whole wheat crackers and coconut pudding (p. 8).

CRISPY FISH FILLETS

230 C (450 F)
Serves 2

2/3 lbs. frozen fish fillets
   (cod or other white fish)
¼ cup fine dry bread crumbs
1/3 cup skim milk
2 tbsp. grated parmesan cheese
margarine

Remove frozen fillets from freezer and allow to soften slightly at room temperature (about 30 minutes). Cut fish into two equal-sized portions using serrated knife. Dip portions into milk, coating well, then into mixture of bread crumbs and cheese. Place on greased baking pan, top with small dab of margarine. Bake 450°F oven for 30 to 35 minutes or just until fish flakes when tested with fork in centre.

Suggestion for completing meal — brown rice, baked squash, and a glass of milk.

PEKING TUNA SALAD

Serves 1

1 tbsp. mayonnaise or salad dressing
1 tsp. finely chopped onions
½ tsp. lemon juice
½ tsp. soya sauce
¼ tsp. curry powder
3¾ oz. can tuna, drained and flaked
2 tbsp. sliced celery or water
   chestnuts

Combine mayonnnaise, onion, lemon juice, soya sauce and curry; blend well. Add tuna and celery and toss mixture gently — chill. Serve in lettuce cups or spread on toast and broil 2 to 3 inches from heat for 3-4 minutes.

Suggestion for completing meal — salad, whole wheat crackers and milk (or if broiling on toast — green salad and milk).

TUNA NOODLE CASSEROLE

180 C (350 F)
Serves 2

1 cup noodles
6½ oz. can tuna
1 can mushroom soup
bread crumbs

Cook noodles according to package direction. Drain. Drain oil from can of tuna and add tuna to noodles. Add mushroom soup (undiluted). Pour into baking dish, sprinkle with bread crumbs and bake for 20 minutes.

OR

Cook on top of stove for 15 minutes on low heat, stirring occasionally and adding milk if necessary.

Peas, mushrooms or cheddar cheese cubes can be added for variety. Chicken, ham, luncheon meat, or wieners may be used instead of tuna.

Suggestion for completing meal — Bert's special salad (p. 15).

Chicken

Chicken is probably the most versatile member of the meat group. On top of the stove try frying, stewing or even steaming it. In the oven, try broiling, roasting or baking it. Include chicken often in your diet. It provides protein, and a significant amount of your daily "B" vitamin needs.

Buying

- For broiled or baked chicken buy grade A even though it is the more expensive; but when the finished product can be disguised by a sauce, use utility grade.
- Utility grade has the same nutritional value as grade A.
- If you have storage space buy whole chickens and have the butcher divide it for you. Most will not charge for this service. Take the entire carcass, as the bony parts can be used for soup.
- If you do not have adequate storage space buy one or two individual chicken parts at a time. Do not be afraid to ask the butcher for smaller quantities than are displayed on the meat counter.
- Poultry is an economical protein buy, all year round. For each serving of cooked poultry buy ½ lb. of meaty chicken parts (eg. legs and thighs or breasts) or ¾ lb. of bony (eg. wings or necks).

Storage

- Both raw and cooked chicken must be frozen if stored more than a day or two. Chicken should be used immediately if it cannot be refrigerated.
- Divide chicken into meal-size portions and place in plastic bags before freezing for easier handling.

SIMPLE SIMON
190 C (375 F)
Serves 1

3/8 lb. chicken (e.g. chicken breast)
2 tbsp. milk
5-8 crackers (whole wheat or cheese)
1/8 tsp. salt

Crush crackers and set aside. Coat chicken pieces with vegetable oil and dip in cracker crumb mixture. Place on baking sheet and bake for 40 minutes.

Suggestion for completing meal — vegetable rice pilaf (p. 33) and milk.

BRAISED CHICKEN LIVERS
Serves 1

2 tbsp. chopped onion
1 tbsp. butter or margarine
2 tbsp. flour
¼ tsp. salt
dash of pepper
¼ lb. chicken livers
Worcestershire sauce to taste
¼ cup water

Melt margarine in frying pan, add onion and brown. While onion is browning mix flour, salt and pepper in a small bowl. Coat chicken livers with flour mixture. Add chicken livers to frying pan, cook until browned on both sides. Add water and Worcestershire sauce, simmer until thickened (you may need to add a little more flour).

Suggestion for completing meal — carrots, whole wheat roll and milk.

ROASTED OR BAKED CHICKEN
165 C (325 F)

Place chicken on small rack (if not available cut holes in an almuinum pie pan and turn it upside down) in a baking dish. For individual servings cover chicken with a tent of aluminum foil to lock in the moisture and prevent drying. Bake at 325°F for about 40-45 minutes. For a whole chicken, bake at 325°F for about 30 minutes per lb. Baste occasionally — meat is done when leg moves freely in the joint.

Suggestion for completing meal — baked squash, bread dressing and milk.

CHICKEN ROSEMARY
180 C (350 F)
Serves 1

1 piece of chicken
1 tsp. vegetable oil
1 tsp. vinegar
3 rosemary leaves

Place chicken in a greased casserole. Sprinkle it with oil, vinegar and rosemary. Place in refrigerator for a few hours to marinate. Bake for one hour.

Suggestion for completing meal — stir-fry vegetables (p. 16), slice of whole wheat bread and a serving of cottage cheese custard.

CHICKEN MUSHROOM CASSEROLE

180 C (350 F)
Serves 2

4 chicken parts
1 can mushroom soup
1 small sliced onion (optional)

Place chicken parts in a greased casserole. Cover with canned mushroom soup (undiluted) and bake for 1 hour. Chicken may be browned in oil with onion prior to the addition of soup if preferred.

Suggestion for completing meal — broccoli and whole wheat dinner rolls.

CHICKEN SOUP

Makes 2 cups

leftover chicken parts
(or 6 wings or 4-6 necks)
½ cup onion
½ cup celery
½ cup carrots
1 tsp. salt
dash of pepper
2 cups water

Use any bony chicken parts such as the leftovers of a chicken after breasts, thighs and legs are removed. (Use 6 chicken wings or 4-6 necks if leftovers are not available). Place chicken, onion, celery, carrots, salt and pepper in a pot. Cover with 2 cups water. Bring to boil. Simmer until tender (about 1 hour). Any leftover chunks of cooked chicken may be added.

Suggestion for completing meal — grilled cheese sandwiches.

OVEN-STEWED CHICKEN

180 C (350 F)
Makes 2½ cups of cut-up cooked chicken

2½ lbs. cut stewing fowl or
    fricassee chicken
1 onion, cut up
1 stalk celery, with leaves
1 carrot cut in chunks
1/8 tsp. poultry seasoning
pinch of salt and pepper

Place chicken pieces in casserole with vegetables. Add water to practically cover (about 2½ cups). Cover tightly and bake at 350°F for about 2½ hours or until chicken is tender. Remove chicken and cool. Skin, and remove meat from bones. Wrap meat well and refrigerate for use in pie or salad. Strain cooking liquid and refrigerate. Skim fat from top before using.

Note: If desired chicken may be stewed in heavy pot on top of stove for the same length of time.

CHICKEN SALAD SUPREME

Serves 1

½ cup diced cooked chicken
2 tbsp. thinly-sliced celery
pinch of salt
½ an orange

½ cup cooked brown rice
1 tbsp. chopped green onion or chives
2 tbsp. salad dressing or yogurt

Combine all ingredients except orange. Peel and slice orange and cut slices in quarters. Stir into salad before serving.

Suggestion for completing meal — cream of mushroom soup and melba toast.

COMPANY CHICKEN PIE

220 C (425 F)
Serves 2

1 cup cooked chicken
3 tbsp. skim milk powder
2 tbsp. flour
2 tbsp. chopped onion
salt and pepper to taste

2/3 cup chicken stock
2 tbsp. chicken fat or margarine
¼ cup chopped celery
½ cup cooked vegetables

Dissolve skim milk powder in chicken stock. Melt fat, blend in flour until smooth. Cook, stirring constantly, over medium heat until smoothly thickened. Cook vegetables until tender-crisp. Add chicken and vegetables to sauce. Season to taste and turn into small casserole dish.

Biscuit Topping

2/3 cup whole wheat flour
¼ tsp. salt
1/3 cup milk

1 tsp. baking powder
2 tbsp. shortening

For biscuit topping, mix flour, baking powder and salt. Mix in shortening with a fork or 2 knives until crumbly. Stir in milk. Mix enough to wet ingredients. Drop dough from a tablespoon onto top of pie making 4 biscuits. Bake at 425°F oven, about 20 minutes or until biscuits are cooked.

Suggestion for completing meal — spinach salad and baked custard.

Whole grain cereals

Bread and other products made from grains and cereals provide B vitamins, iron, protein and dietary fibre (or roughage).

Some of the major vitamins and iron are lost in processing, but are replaced in "enriched" cereal products.

Buying

Some nutritious economical choices:
- whole wheat bread and rolls
- bran muffins
- bran cereals
- oatmeal
- shredded wheat
- rye, whole wheat and graham crackers
- "day old" bread
- brown and/or converted rice
- macaroni, noodles and spaghetti that contain "enriched" flour.

Storage

- bread keeps best in cool dry place
- flour, corn meal, rice and rolled oats should be stored in jars or cans with tight fitting lids.

SKILLET BANNOCK

Makes 6 wedges

2/3 cup whole wheat flour
1/3 cup all-purpose flour
1½ tsp. baking powder
¼ tsp. salt
3 tbsp. skim milk powder
¼ cup raisins
½ cup + 1 tbsp. water
1-2 tsp. oil

Mix dry ingredients. Stir in raisins. Add water gradually and stir well. Heat 1 tsp. oil in a 7" cast-iron skillet. Spread batter in pan and cook over **low** heat for 10 minutes, until golden brown. Turn and cook 4-5 minutes on flip side — add more oil if necessary.

Remove from pan and cool slightly. Cut into wedges and serve warm with butter and fruit preserves.

Suggestion for completing meal — tomato lentil soup (p. 20) and a glass of milk.

HEALTH BREAD

230 C (425 F)
Makes 2 loaves

2 cups skim milk
4 tbsp. oil
¼ cup molasses
1 tbsp. salt
1 yeast cake
½ cup lukewarm water
1 tsp. sugar
5½ cups whole wheat flour
4 tbsp. wheat germ

Scald milk and place in a large bowl. Add oil, molasses and salt and cool to lukewarm. Dissolve yeast in ½ cup lukewarm water in which 1 tsp. sugar has been dissolved. Let stand for 15 minutes than add to the milk mixture. Stir in about 3 cups whole wheat flour until smooth. Add wheat germ, continue adding flour until stiff enough to knead. Knead for 5-7 minutes and place in a greased bowl. Cover with a towel. Let rise at room temperature until double in bulk.

Once it is double in bulk, knead again for 2 minutes. Divide into 2 portions and shape into loaves. Place in greased tins and let rise to double in bulk again. Bake for 15 minutes at 230°C (425°F). Reduce heat to 180°C (350°F) and bake until done, approximately 45-55 minutes.

Suggestions for completing meal — split pea soup and cheese and pears for dessert.

PANCAKES

Makes 3-5" pancakes

½ cup pancake mix (buy the type that needs only water or use the mix below)
2 tbsp. bran

Put pancake mix into a bowl, add bran, add water according to package directions, and stir the batter. Heat a little (1 teaspoon) oil or margarine in the frying pan, and pour in batter to make pancakes. Turn them when bubbles have formed across the pancake. Brown other side. This recipe makes three 5 inch pancakes.

Note: To increase protein, add 2 tablespoons skim milk powder.

Suggestion for completing meal — sausage, ½ grapefruit.

PANCAKE MIX

2 cups flour (whole wheat)
1 tbsp. baking powder
1 tbsp. sugar
½ cup skim milk powder

Mix ingredients together. Will keep indefinitely stored in a jar. When ready to use mix ½ cup pancake mix with 1/3 cup plus 1 tsp. water.

When you feel creative:

You can add one or two of the following foods to the basic pancake mix above before you cook it:
- slices of fruit (apples or banana) or berries
- oatmeal or cornmeal
- peanut butter
- chopped ham or bacon
- grated cheddar cheese

Then to top of pancake, instead of sugar syrup which adds only calories, try one of the following:
- sliced fruit
- yogurt, plain or with fruit
- apple sauce
- yogurt mixed with undiluted frozen orange juice concentrate

FOUR WEEK BRAN MUFFINS   200 C (400 F)

This recipe for batter will last in your refrigerator for 4 weeks; you can bake some muffins whenever you like and return the rest to the refrigerator.

1 cup boiling water
1 cup bran
½ cup oil
1 cup brown sugar
2 eggs
2 cups buttermilk
2¾ cups flour
1½ tsp. salt
2½ tsp. baking soda
1 cup raisins
2 cups bran flakes

Pour boiling water over bran — let stand. Meanwhile, cream together oil and sugar and add the eggs. Blend buttermilk into shortening mixture. Add the bran and water mixture. Sift together flour, salt, soda and stir into the above mixture. Add raisins and bran flakes. Store in the refrigerator in a container with a lid (a plastic ice cream pail works well; it can also be used to mix ingredients). Refrigerate at least 24 hours before baking. When you want some fresh baked muffins remove some of the batter without stirring. Bake in greased muffin tins or custard cups filling each cup two thirds full. Bake at 400°F for 20-25 minutes.

DROP CHEESE BISCUITS

230 C (450 F)
Makes 4 biscuits

2/3 cup unsifted flour (whole wheat)
1 tsp. baking powder
¼ tsp. salt
2 tbsps. shortening
1/3 cup milk
2 tbsp. grated cheddar cheese

Mix flour, baking powder, salt and cheese. Mix in shortening with a fork or two knives until crumbly. Stir in milk. Mix enough to wet dry ingredients. Drop dough from a tablespoon on a greased baking pan. Bake at 450°F (very hot oven) 10-12 minutes until lightly browned.

VEGETABLE RICE PILAF

Serves 2

1/3 cup uncooked converted rice
1 tbsp. chopped onion
3 tbsp. butter or margarine
1 chicken bouillon cube
1-8 oz. can mixed vegetables
   (or 1 cup left over vegetables)
1 cup water

Cook rice and onion in butter 5-10 minutes or till lightly browned, stirring frequently. Add water, bouillon cube and salt. Bring to boil, stirring to dissolve bouillon cube. Reduce heat, cover, and cook slowly about 20 minutes or till liquid is absorbed and rice is fluffy. Drain vegetables and stir in; heat through.

Suggestion for completing meal — grilled liver and a dessert of bananas topped with yogurt.

GRANOLA

150 C (300 F)
Makes 6 cups

3 cups rolled oats
¼ cup wheat germ
¼ cup bran
½ cup sunflower seeds
¼ cup sesame seeds
¼ cup skim milk powder
¼ cup vegetable oil
½ cup orange juice concentrate

Mix all ingredients together so that the dry ingredients are coated with the vegetable oil and the orange juice concentrate. Spread this mixture evenly on a cookie sheet. Bake for 40 minutes or until crisp. During baking, stir every 15 minutes to ensure even browning. After baking add:

½ cup raisins
¼ cup unsweetened coconut

Store granola in cupboard in a jar with a tight-fitting lid. Use ½ cup granola per serving.

Suggestion for completing meal — milk for cereal, boiled egg and a glass of orange juice.

THREE-GRAIN BISCUITS

160 C (325 F)
Makes 16 cookies

¼ cup all-purpose flour
¼ cup quick-cooking oats
½ cup whole wheat flour
¼ cup wheat germ
¼ cup margarine
3 tbsp. cold water

1/8 tsp. baking soda
pinch of salt
1 tbsp. skim milk powder
2 tbsp. sugar
½ tsp. vanilla

Combine all-purpose flour, oats, whole wheat flour, wheat germ, baking soda, salt, skim milk powder and granulated sugar in a large bowl. Cut in margarine with pastry blender or knife until the size of small peas. Combine vanilla with water and sprinkle over, mixing enough to make dough pack together into a ball. Knead slightly if necessary. Pat and flatten on lightly-floured board. Roll to 1/8″ thickness. Cut out with 2½ inch floured cutter. Bake on greased baking sheets, about ½ inch apart in 325°F oven, about 20 to 25 minutes. Watch them because they should not brown at all.

Suggestion for completing meal — raw vegetable stick, cheese, and a glass of milk.

These are good for a knapsack lunch.

IRISH BRAN BREAD

200 C (400 F)
Makes 1 loaf

½ cup corn meal
1 cup 100% bran
3 cups whole wheat flour
½ cup all-purpose flour

¾ tsp. salt
1½ tsp. baking soda
1½ tsp. cream of tartar
2 cups buttermilk

Measure corn meal, bran, and whole wheat flour into a bowl and stir to mix. Measure all-purpose flour, salt, baking soda and cream of tartar into sieve and sift into bowl, containing first three ingredients. Mix thoroughly. Make a well in dry ingredients and add buttermilk all at once. Stir to mix. If too sticky add more flour. Shape dough with floured hands and press into greased 9 x 5 inch loaf pan. Bake at 400°F for about one hour. Let cool in pan for 10 minutes, then turn out on wire rack to finish cooling.

Note: Quick-cooking oats may be substituted for bran. Reconstituted powdered buttermilk may be used in place of fresh buttermilk.

Suggestion for completing meal — orange juice, soft cooked egg, and coffee au lait.

APPLE BRAN MUFFINS

180 C (350 F)
Makes 12 2" muffins

1 cup whole wheat flour
¼ tsp. salt
½ tbsp. grated orange rind
¼ cup raisins
juice of ½ an orange
1 egg (beaten)
1 tbsp. oil

¾ cup wheat bran
¼ tsp. nutmeg
½ cup chopped apple
¼ cup chopped nuts or sunflower seeds
1 cup buttermilk or sour milk
¼ cup molasses

Preheat oven to 350°F. Toss flour, bran, salt, and nutmeg together with a fork. Stir in orange rind, apples, raisins and nuts or seeds. Pour the juice of ½ an orange into a 2 cup measure and add buttermilk to make 1 cup. Add to egg, molasses and oil and stir thoroughly. Pour into greased muffin tins filling them 2/3 full and bake for 25 minutes.

Suggestion for a snack — slice of Jack cheese.

DILL BREAD

180 C (350 F)
2 loaves

2 pkg. yeast (1½ tbsp.)
2 tsp. sugar
½ cup chopped onion
3 tbsp. oil
1½ cup evaporated milk
½ cup chopped parsley
1 cup white flour (approx.)

3 tbsp. sugar
1 tsp. salt
½ tsp. dried dillweed
¼ tsp. sage
1 cup cornmeal
3 cups whole wheat flour

Soften yeast in ½ cup warm water and 2 tsp. sugar. Cook onion in hot oil until tender. Remove from heat and add milk (to warm it). In bread bowl combine yeast and milk mixtures with parsley, remaining sugar, salt, dill, sage, cornmeal and two cups of whole wheat flour. Mix well. Add remaining whole wheat flour and enough white flour to make a moderately soft dough. Knead on floured surface for 5 minutes. Place in greased bowl and let rise till double, about 1 hour. Punch down and divide in half. Place in 2 well greased 1 pound coffee cans. Cover and let rise until double, about 30-45 minutes. Bake in 350°F oven for 45 minutes.

Suggestion for completing meal — cottage cheese stuffed tomato (p. 11), and sardines.

WHOLE WHEAT SODA BREAD

190 C (375 F)
Makes 1 small round loaf

1 cup sifted all-purpose flour
1½ tsp. baking powder
1 tbsp. sugar
1/8 cup of shortening
¾ cup buttermilk
½ tsp. salt
½ tsp. soda
1 cup whole wheat flour
1 egg

Heat oven to 375°F. Lightly grease one 8" round layer-cake pan. Sift all-purpose flour, salt, baking powder, soda and sugar into a mixing bowl. Add whole wheat flour and mix in lightly with a fork. Add shortening and cut in finely. Beat egg and buttermilk together with a fork and add to dry ingredients. Stir just until blended. Turn out on floured board and knead lightly until smooth, about 20 strokes. Shape into a round and place into the prepared pan and pat down so that it fills the pan. Cut 3 slashes across the top of each loaf making the cuts about ½" deep. Bake 25 to 30 minutes or until loaves are well browned and sound hollow when tapped on top. Serve warm or cold.

CRUSTY POPOVERS

200 C (400 F)

1 egg
2½ tbsp. skim milk powder
1/3 cup water
2 greased custard cups
1 tbsp. melted margarine
1/8 tsp. salt
1/3 cup whole wheat flour

Beat egg until light, add skim milk powder, water, melted margarine and salt. Blend well. Gradually beat in flour. Fill each cup 2/3 full of batter. Bake 50-60 minutes or until popovers are high, crusty and well browned. Remove from cups at once and cut slit in each to allow steam to escape. Serve hot.

Suggestion for completing meal — hearty beef stew (p. 52) and milk.

Ethnic ideas

Ethnic foods add variety and interest to your daily menu. For example, there are curries from India, perogies from the Ukraine, pasta dishes from Italy, vegetable dishes from China and Japan, and chili from Mexico.

The selection of delicious and unusual foods from other cultures are indeed numerous and they can easily be incorporated in your menus. Remember your 4 Food Groups checklist to ensure a balanced meal.

We've chosen two Chinese recipes for top of the stove cooking. Both recipes utilize the "stir fry" method of cookery. It is quick and easy and the results are indeed worthwhile! The stir fry method involves cooking foods quickly at high heat while stirring. Oil is used to prevent sticking but the amount can easily be controlled, especially if you are calorie conscious.

The availability of the food supplies for these two recipes is good, in fact most grocery stores would supply all these foods and, if not, alternatives work just as well.

Don't worry about needing special equipment and utensils. All you need is a frying pan and a wooden spoon.

BROCCOLI AND BEEF

Serves 2

½ cup broccoli
6 oz. beef, raw (flank, round or chuck)
½ tsp. soya sauce

1 tsp. cornstarch
dash sugar
dash salt
2 tbsp. oil

Slice the raw beef into thin strips ¾" x 2½" x 1/8" thick. Combine beef with 1 tbsp. oil, ¼ tsp. soya sauce and a dash of sugar in a small bowl. Let marinate 30 minutes. Cut broccoli into serving sizes by cutting stalk and flowers in half lengthwise and 3 inches long. In a small bowl combine ¼ tsp. soya sauce, 1 tsp. cornstarch and 1 tbsp. water. Heat the pan on high heat. Add broccoli. Stir fry. Cook until bright green about 1 minute. Then add ¼ cup water, cover and cook for 2-3 minutes. Transfer broccoli to a plate. Add 1 tbsp. oil and beef to hot pan. Stir fry beef until all the redness disappears (30-60 seconds). Add broccoli and season with salt. Make clearing in centre of pan. Add cornstarch mixture, stirring constantly. Bring to boil until sauce is thickened. Serve immediately.

Suggestion for completing meal — rice and yogurt for dessert.

CABBAGE ROLLS

180 C (350 F)
Serves 2

½ cup cooked coverted rice
1 tbsp. butter or margarine
2 tbsp. onion, finely chopped
¼ lb. ground beef

7 or 8 cabbage leaves
1 tsp. salt
½ cup tomato juice

Brown ground beef. Remove from pan and fry onion until golden brown. Mix onion, beef and rice together — cool. Place cabbage in rapidly boiling water for 2 minutes. Drain carefully. Grease a covered casserole or roaster. Place two cabbage leaves on the bottom. Place a spoonful of rice filling on 3 or 4 cabbage leaves and roll up, folding ends in tightly. Arrange cabbage rolls in casserole, dot with margarine and sprinkle with salt. Pour tomato juice over cabbage rolls. Place other two leaves on the top to prevent scorching. Cover tightly and bake at 350°F for one hour. If covered pan isn't available use tin foil tightly crimped over pan.

Suggestion for completing meal — yogurt and peaches.

GREEK SALAD

Serves 2

2 cups torn lettuce, spinach or other salad greens
1 tomato, cut in wedges
1 green onion, chopped

2 tbsp. oil and vinegar dressing (homemade)
2 tbsp. crumbled feta cheese
black olives (optional)

Combine salad greens, tomato and green onion in salad bowl. Toss with oil and vinegar dressing. Top with black olives, if being used, and sprinkle with feta cheese.

Suggestion for completing meal — lentil and rice casserole.

MOUSSAKA
180 C (350 F)
Serves 2

1 small zucchini	1 tbsp. oil
3 oz. ground beef	1 tbsp. flour
½ crushed clove of garlic (optional)	½ cup milk
¼ cup chopped onion	1 beaten egg
2 tsp. flour	1/8 tsp. nutmeg
¼ tsp. cinnamon, oregano, and salt	pinch of salt
1/8 tsp. nutmeg and pepper	pinch of pepper
¼ cup catsup	2 tbsp. grated parmesan cheese
½ cup stewed tomatoes cut up	

Cut zucchini lengthwise or crosswise and panfry in just enough oil to keep it from sticking until slightly softened. Remove zucchini from pan. Put ground beef and onion in pan and brown. Add garlic and 2 tsp. flour. Add ½ tsp. cinnamon, oregano and salt, 1/8 tsp. nutmeg and pepper, catsup and stewed tomatoes. Cook over medium heat. While meat sauce cooks, prepare custard topping as follows: Mix 1 tbsp. oil, 1 tbsp. flour and ½ cup milk in a pan. Add beaten egg, nutmeg and pinch of salt and pepper. Stir over medium heat until well blended — about 1 minute. Remove from heat and add grated parmesan cheese.

In a greased casserole, place half of cooked zucchini. Spoon meat sauce on top and spread evenly. Arrange remaining zucchini on top of this and spread custard evenly over all. Bake for 30 minutes or until the custard is bubbly and the centre appears firm.

Suggestion for completing meal — a whole wheat roll.

BORSCHT
Serves 2

½ cup shredded beets	¼ cup shredded cabbage
½ cup chopped carrots	1 tsp. margarine or butter
¼ cup chopped onion	1 tsp. lemon juice
¾ cup boiling water	dash of pepper
¼ tsp. salt	dash of dillweed, if desired
¾ cup beef stock	
(1 bouillon cube + ¾ cup water)	

Cook beets, carrots, onions, boiling water and salt uncovered for 20 minutes. Add beef stock, cabbage and margarine and cook uncovered another 15 minutes. Add lemon juice, pepper and dillweed if used. Pour into soup bowls. Serve topped with yogurt.

Suggestion for completing meal — meat sandwich and vanilla pudding for dessert.

INDIAN CURRY
Serves 1

    1 tbsp. vegetable oil   1 tbsp. enriched flour
    1 small onion, chopped   1 cup hot water
    1 tsp. curry powder   ¾-1 cup cooked meat or fish
    dash chili powder   (lamb, chicken, shrimp, etc.)

Fry onion in oil. Blend curry powder, chili powder and flour into oil and onion mixture. Slowly add the water. Simmer gently for 15 minutes. Add the meat and heat through.

Suggestion for completing meal — rice, cucumber and tomato slices with cottage cheese custard (p. 42) for dessert.

EGG FOO YONG
Serves 1

    ¼ cup bean sprouts — rinsed and drained   2 tbsp. thawed frozen peas
    ¼ cup cooked meat — sliced into slivers   1-2 eggs, slightly beaten
        or diced   vegetable oil
    2 tbsp. onion — sliced into thin slivers   salt

Heat frying pan on high heat. Add 1 tbsp. oil. Add onions, stir fry 15-30 seconds. Add celery to onions, stir fry 15-30 seconds, and bean sprouts to onion mixture — stir fry 30-60 seconds. Salt to taste. Pour in beaten eggs. Stir until eggs start to set. Turn over and serve.

Variations: Substitute the vegetables used, eg. use celery, broccoli, carrots, cauliflower or snow peas, sliced into thin slivers.

Suggestion for completing meal — converted rice and a glass of milk.

LEN'S IRISH "CHILI"
Serves 2

    3 oz. lean ground beef   ¼ cup diced celery
       (or lean ground pork or veal)   ½ small garlic clove, crushed and chopped
    1 cup kidney beans   (optional)
    ½ cup chopped onion   1 tsp. chili powder
    1 cup stewed tomatoes   ¼ tsp. salt and pinch of pepper

Saute meat until browned. Add onion and garlic and cook for 5 minutes. Add celery, kidney beans and their liquid, stewed tomatoes, chili powder, salt and pepper. Simmer for 30 minutes.

Suggestion for completing meal — whole wheat toast and yogurt for dessert.

desserts and snacks

Desserts are a popular addition to any meal and often the best desserts are those you make yourself. As well as adding a nice finishing touch to a meal, desserts can add extra food value if their ingredients are chosen from the four food groups. Fruits, eggs, cereal products and milk products can all be incorporated into taste-tempting desserts.

ORANGE FREEZE

Serves 2

    1/8 cup undiluted frozen orange juice   ½ tsp. vanilla
    5/8 cup (5 ounces) plain yogurt   1 tsp. honey

Combine orange juice, yogurt, vanilla and honey. Mix quickly and freeze.

Suggestion for completing meal — tuna fish casserole (p. 25).

BAKED COTTAGE CHEESE CUSTARD (A Calcium Booster)

180 C (350 F)
Serves 2

    1 egg, beaten   ¼ cup raisins
    2/3 cup milk   1/8 tsp. vanilla
    1/3 cup cottage cheese   2 tsp. sugar

Combine egg, milk, sugar, salt and vanilla in a small bowl. Mash cottage cheese slightly with a fork. Add cottage cheese and raisins to first mixture. Pour into individual custard cups and sprinkle with nutmeg. Place baking dish into a deep pan which has hot water, about 2 inches deep, in it. Bake at 250°F for 45 minutes to one hour. When done, a knife inserted in the middle will come out clean. Chill and serve.

Suggestion for completing meal — meat loaf, (p. 47), rice and green beans or peas.

STEWED PRUNES

Serves 1

    8 dried prunes   2 tsp. sugar (optional)
    ¾ cup cold water

Place prunes and water in a saucepan and bring to boiling point. Reduce heat and simmer gently for 20 minutes. Add sugar and cook 10 minutes longer. Add a bit of lemon or a stick of cinnamon for extra flavor if you wish.

Suggestion for completing meal — salmon french toast (p. 22).

FRUIT CRISP

190 C (375 F)
Serves 1

    ½ cup clean and cut up fruit,   1 tbsp. brown sugar
      eg. rhubarb or apple   1½ tsp. flour
    1 tbsp. sugar   ¼ cup rolled oats
    ½ tsp. enriched flour   ¼ tsp. cinnamon if apples or peaches
    1½ tsp. melted margarine   are used.

Place fruit in greased baking pan, sprinkle with mixture of 1 tbsp. sugar and ½ tsp. flour. Next melt margarine and combine brown sugar and 1½ tsp. flour, rolled oats and cinnamon if used. Sprinkle mixture on top of fruit and bake at 375°F until golden brown.

Suggestion for completing meal — chicken salad supreme (p. 29).

FRUIT WHIP
Serves 1

    1 egg white   ½ cup fruit pulp
    pinch of salt   (leftover cooked, canned or pureed fruit)
    2 tbsp. sugar

Add pinch of salt to egg white. Beat until stiff, gradually adding 2 tbsp. sugar while beating. Fold in ½ cup fruit pulp. Place in serving dish and chill for 1 hour before serving.

Suggestion for completing meal — cheese souffle (p. 7).

QUICK FRUIT CRUNCH
Makes 1½ cups

    2 tbsp. margarine   ¼ cup raisins
    1 cup uncooked quick-cooking oats   1/8 tsp. cinnamon
    1 tbsp. brown sugar   ½ cup applesauce or other stewed fruit

For topping, melt margarine in small skillet. Add oats and toast over medium heat, stirring constantly, until golden brown. Stir in sugar, raisins, and cinnamon. Cool and store in covered container in a cool place. At serving time sprinkle two tbsp. topping over applesauce in serving dish.

Suggestion for completing meal — tuna sandwich on whole wheat bread and a glass of milk.

CUSTARD SAUCE (For topping fruit)
Makes 1 cup

    1 egg   ¼ tsp. vanilla
    2/3 cup skim milk   cinnamon, nutmeg or grated orange rind
    1 tsp. sugar

Beat egg well; stir in skim milk; and add sugar. Cook over low heat, stirring constantly, until thickened, about 10 to 15 minutes. Mixture should coat a metal spoon. Remove from heat and add vanilla. Season with spices or orange rind. Cook and refrigerate in covered container.

Snacks

Like desserts, snacks can be a useful way of adding nutritional value to your daily diet. How can you determine which foods make wise snack choices? Pick foods that are low in sugar, and that are from the four food groups. Cheese, whole grain or enriched breads and crackers, cold meats, nuts, milk or milk drinks, fruits and vegetables and juices would all be nutritious snacks. If you are watching your weight, raw vegetables and unsweetened fruit or vegetable juices, low fat milk, and cottage cheese would be recommended.

ORANGE RAISIN SCONES

200 C (400 F)
Makes 16

½ cup raisins
½ cup orange juice
1½ cups whole wheat flour, unsifted
1 medium egg
2 tbsp. sugar

2 tsp. baking powder
½ tsp. cream of tartar
¼ tsp. salt
¼ cup margarine

Soak raisins in orange juice. Measure sugar, flour, baking powder, cream of tartar and salt into a large bowl. Stir well to mix. Cut margarine into dry ingredients using a pastry blender or two knives, until the size of peas. Add the egg, raisins and orange juice and give a few stirs to mix and blend. Shape dough into a ball. (If dough is too sticky knead in a little more flour). Divide dough in half and pat on floured board into ½ inch thick round. Cut each round into sixths and place them on a greased cookie sheet. Bake in 400°F oven about 12 minutes.

TANGY VEGETABLE DIP

2 oz. plain yogurt
1 tbsp. mayonnaise

½ tsp. sweet pickle relish

Combine yogurt, mayonnaise and relish. Use as a dip for a variety of raw vegetables: carrots, celery, green pepper, turnip, cherry tomato, cauliflower, etc.

TUNA CHEESE BUN

Serves 1

2 tbsp. tuna fish
1½ tsp. mayonnaise
1 tsp. chopped green pepper, celery or onion

dash of Worcestershire sauce
½ hamburger bun (or slice of bread)
1 tbsp. grated cheese

Combine tuna fish, mayonnaise, green pepper (celery or onion) and Worcestershire sauce. Mix well. Spread this mixture onto the bun. Sprinkle with grated cheese. Place on a pan and put under broiler until cheese melts. Serve hot.

Note: If bread is used, place under the broiler for one minute, turn over and broil one minute more. Then top with tuna, and follow recipe directions.

Beverages

PIQUANT TOMATO JUICE COCKTAIL
Serves 1

 6 oz. chilled tomato juice   dash Worcestershire sauce
 ½ tsp. lemon juice   celery salt to taste

Mix together tomato juice, lemon juice, Worcestershire sauce and celery salt. Stir thoroughly and enjoy

ORANGE NOG
Serves 1

 6 oz. unsweetened orange juice   1½ tbsp. skim milk powder

Mix orange juice and skim milk powder together. Stir well and serve with ice.

APPLE ORANGE TODDY
Serves 1

 ½ cup apple juice   ground cinnamon stick
 ¼ cup orange juice   orange slice, (optional)

Heat juices in saucepan just until hot, do not boil. Pour into heated mug and sprinkle with cinnamon or add cinnamon stick stirrer. Float an orange slice on top.

Variations: add a dash of vanilla or rum flavoring.

MEXICAN CHOCOLATE
Serves 2

 2 cups water   3 inches of cinnamon stick OR
 ½ cup + 3 tbsp. dry skim milk powder   ¼ tsp. powdered cinnamon
 2 tbsp. cocoa   ½ tsp. vanilla
 2 tbsp. sugar

Using 2 tbsp. of water make a paste with cocoa and sugar. In small saucepan combine water, dry milk, cinnamon and cocoa paste. Cook over medium heat, stirring constantly until mixture is heated through. Remove from heat and add vanilla. Remove the cinnamon stick if one was used. Beat mixture vigorously with fork or egg whisk until frothy. Serve in warmed mugs.

Entertaining cheaply

Entertaining can be fun and having company over for a meal certainly adds a little zest to the day. Extra time, energy and equipment are not necessary if the menu is chosen wisely.

You may wish to choose any of the recipes and menus suggested in this booklet or you may wish to choose your own menu.

NEVER FAIL CHEESE SOUFFLE

180 C (350 F)
Serves 2

2 tbsp. quick cooking tapioca
pinch of salt
¾ cup reconstituted skim milk powder
½ cup grated cheese
2 well beaten egg yolks
2 stiffly beaten egg whites

Combine tapioca, salt, milk in a saucepan and let stand 5 minutes. Bring to a boil, stirring constantly. Remove from heat and add cheese and stir until melted. Add cheese mixture to the egg yolks and mix well. Fold in egg whites. Pour into two greased casseroles approximately 8 oz. each or 1 slightly larger sized casserole approximately 20 oz. and place casserole in a pan of hot water. Bake for 30 minutes or until set.

Suggestion for completing meal — broccoli and a bran muffin.

EGGS DELIGHT

Serves 2

1 tbsp. butter or margarine
1 tbsp. enriched flour
½ cup milk
¼ cup grated cheese
salt to taste
1 medium tomato, sliced
2 eggs
2 slices of bread

Melt butter in saucepan, add flour and cook for 3 minutes stirring constantly. Add milk slowly, continue stirring until thickened. Next add cheese. Cook, stirring for 2 minutes or until cheese melts. Salt to taste. Keep warm.

Poach the eggs. Toast two slices of bread. Place the tomato slices on the toast and put the eggs on top of tomato. Top with cheese sauce. Garnish with a shake of pepper and a sprig of parsley.

For variety: use cooked asparagus or spinach instead of tomato.

Suggestion for completing meal — a steaming cup of Mexican chocolate.

SPECIAL MEAT LOAF

180 C (350 F)
Serves 2

½ lb. ground beef
2 tbsp. dry milk
1 egg
¼ cup bread crumbs
onion
salt
Worcestershire sauce (optional)
tomato juice or catsup

Mix all ingredients together, adding sufficient tomato juice or catsup to moisten. Pack into a small loaf pan or casserole or make individual servings in a muffin tin. Bake for 30 minutes.

Suggestion for completing meal — coleslaw, whole wheat bread and cheese.

WALDORF SALAD

Serves 1

1 small apple diced, unpeeled
2 tbsp. seedless raisins
1 tbsp. salad dressing (or enough to moisten)
¼ cup chopped celery
2 tbsp. walnuts

Combine all ingredients and refrigerate.

Suggestion for completing meal — peanut butter on whole grain crackers and a glass of milk.

ORIENTAL CHICKEN

180 C (350 F)
Serves 2

1 chicken breast split in half
1½ tsp. cornstarch
1½ tsp. cold water
2 tbsp. soya sauce
1 small can pineapple rings
1 tbsp. vinegar
1 tbsp. sugar
dash of garlic powder
dash of pepper
dash of ground ginger

Remove skin from chicken breast. Coat chicken with a little oil, place in pan and brown under broiler. Combine cornstarch, cold water in a small saucepan. Add to this sugar, soya sauce, 2 tbsp. of pineapple juice from the can of pineapple rings, vinegar, salt, pepper and garlic powder.

Cook sauce over medium heat stirring constantly until the sauce thickens. Pour the sauce over browned chicken and bake at 350°F for 30 minutes, basting occasionally. Next place two pineapple rings under each chicken breast, and continue baking for 30 minutes more. Serve garnished with a sprig of parsley and tomato slices.

Variations: use chicken or turkey pieces instead of chicken breasts. Use any type of fruit instead of pineapple rings.

Suggestion for completing meal — baked rice and a glass of milk, or a serving of coconut pudding (p. 8).

POLYNESIAN CHICKEN

Serves 2

½ cup drained pineapple tidbits (reserve juice)
2 tbsp. brown sugar
2 tbsp. vinegar
¼ cup green pepper strips
pinch of salt
dash of soya sauce, (optional)
2 tsp. cornstarch
½ cup pineapple juice (or pineapple and orange)
½ medium onion, sliced very thinly
1½ cups cooked chicken, but into strips or chunks

Blend cornstarch in pineapple juice in saucepan. Add brown sugar, vinegar, and salt. Heat, stirring constantly, until thickened and clear. Add onion and green pepper. Simmer blend flavors. Add chicken and heat to serving temperature.

Suggestion for completing meal — rice and a glass of milk.

BAKED RICE

180 C (350 F)
Serves 2

½ cup brown rice
2 tsp. melted butter
1 cup boiling water
½ pkg. dry onion soup mix

Put rice in casserole and pour melted butter over the top. Mix until rice is coated with butter. Pour boiling water over rice and sprinkle with onion soup mix. Cover and bake for 45 minutes or until rice is tender and all water is absorbed.

Suggestion for completing meal — baked fish fillets (p. 22), saucy vegetables (p. 13).

OATMEAL COOKIES ROYALE

1 egg beaten
½ cup margarine or butter
1 cup chopped dates
¼ cup coconut
1 tsp. vanilla
2 cups rolled oats
¼ cup sugar

In a heavy skillet, combine beaten eggs, margarine, sugar and chopped dates. Cook until the dates pull away cleanly from the side of the skillet. Add coconut, vanilla and rolled oats. Mix thoroughly. Allow to cook somewhat. Press in a lightly greased 8" square pan. Cool and cut in squares for instant cookies. A nutritious snack.

CHEESE AND APPLES

Cut apples into slices (leave skin on). Cut cheese into cubes, insert a toothpick in each cube. Arrange attractively on a plate. Pass around napkins and enjoy.

This snack can be as simple or as elegant as you like to make it. The possibilities are endless. Just a few ideas include:

several types of cheese
carrot sticks
celery sticks
pickles
whole wheat crackers
orange segments
ham cubes
tomato wedges
green pepper sticks, etc.

TROPICAL FRUIT SALAD

Serves 2

½ cup cubed pineapple or melon
1 orange, peeled and cubed
1 banana, sliced
3 tbsp. toasted unsweetened coconut or chopped nuts

Combine all ingredients except coconut. Put in two dishes and top with coconut.

Suggestion for completing meal — never-fail souffle (p. 47) and tea biscuits.

CHICKEN BREASTS IN ORANGE JUICE

180 C (350 F)
Serves 2

2 celery stalks
1 orange cut in sections
½ cup orange juice
2 chicken breasts

Bone chicken, cut celery in ½ inch pieces. Arrange chicken and celery in shallow baking pan. Top with orange sections. Pour juice over. Bake covered for 30 minutes at 350oF.

This is also good to eat cold. Prepare the day before a picnic if you wish.

Suggestion for completing meal — green salad, dill bread with a slice of cheese.

Cooking on a shoestring

Cooking without a proper kitchen can be a real problem. If you find yourself eating out a lot, eating poorly, or spending more on food than you can afford, then this section is for you. It is possible to have nutritious meals and snacks in a furnished room even though there is no stove, refrigerator, and only a little money for food.

All the recipes below are simple, nutritious, inexpensive and can be prepared without an oven. These suggestions will hopefully launch you on some creative recipe ideas of your own.

MACKEREL WITH TOMATOES

Serves 2

1 tbsp. vegetable oil
1 tbsp. onion, sliced
1 cup canned tomatoes
½ cup water
1 small carrot, sliced

1 clove garlic chopped
1 bay leaf, (optional)
salt and pepper
1-7 oz. tin mackerel, well drained

Heat oil in frying pan. Add the onion and garlic, cook them until soft and golden. (If you don't have a garlic clove, you can use garlic powder which would be added with the salt and pepper). Next add the tomatoes, water, carrot, bay leaf and salt and pepper to the onions. Simmer at low heat for 25 minutes. Mash the bones and break the fish into chunks. Add fish and bones to vegetable sauce. Let fish heat through.

Suggestion for completing meal — enriched noodles, lettuce leaf topped with cottage cheese.

HAMBURGER VEGETABLE CHOWDER

Serves 2

¼ lb. ground beef
¼ cup canned tomatoes
1 small carrot, diced
½ stalk celery, diced
½ small onion, chopped

¼ cup pearl barley
1 small potato, cubed
1½ cups water
salt and pepper

Brown the ground beef over medium heat, drain off excess fat. Add carrots, celery, onion, barley, potatoes and water, salt and pepper to taste. Simmer for about 1 hour until the barley is tender.

Suggestion for completing meal — whole wheat roll and cheese wedge.

HEARTY BEEF STEW

Serves 1

2 tsp. vegetable oil
3/8 lb. stewing beef
¾ cup hot water
1 sliced onion

1 carrot, quatered
1 potato, quartered
1 tbsp. flour
salt

Heat oil in heavy saucepan. Add stewing beef and brown on all sides. Add water and dash of salt. Bring to a boil. Cover and simmer about 1 hour. Cool and skim off hardened fat. Return to heat and add onions, carrots and potatoes. Cook 30 minutes until vegetables are tender. Mix flour and ½ cup cold water by shaking in a small jar. Add to stew. Stir until it has boiled for 1 minute and is thickened.

Suggestion for completing meal — drop cheese biscuits and a glass of milk.

EGG TOMATO CUP

180 C (350 F)
Serves 1

- 1 egg
- 1 large firm tomato
- 2 tbsp. crisp crumbled bacon or chopped ham
- salt and pepper
- bread crumbs

Cut a slice from stem end of tomato and hollow out pulp. Line bottom of tomato "cup" with chopped bacon or ham. Slip an egg into the tomato cup. Sprinkle with salt and pepper and top with crumbs. Bake until egg is set.

Suggestion for completing meal — a whole wheat roll and a glass of milk.

BILL'S OMELETTE

Serves 1

- 2 eggs
- 2 tbsp. milk
- dash of salt and pepper
- 1 tbsp. butter or margarine
- ¼ cup chopped cooked meat or cheese (ham, bacon, roast chicken)

In a mixing bowl, beat with fork two eggs, 2 tbsp. milk and dash of salt and pepper. Add cooked meat or cheese. Heat 1 tbsp. butter or margarine in skillet until it just sizzles. Pour in egg mixture; turn heat to low. During cooking, lift edges and tip pan so uncooked mixture flows underneath. Do not stir. Cook until entire omelette is set; turn out. Serve immediately.

Suggestion for completing meal — toast, sliced orange and a glass of milk.

QUICK TOMATO MANWICH

Serves 1

- 3 oz. lean ground beef
- 1 small tomato (cubed)
- 1 tbsp. mayonnaise
- 2 tsp. pickle relish
- dash of salt and pepper
- 1 tsp. prepared mustard

Brown meat, stirring frequently and add remaining ingredients. Heat thoroughly. Serve over toasted whole wheat bun.

Suggestion for completing meal — a glass of milk.

SPANISH RICE
Serves 2

½ cup raw brown rice
2 tbsp. chopped onion
½ cup vegetable stock
1 stalk celery
few drops of vegetable oil

½ cup canned tomatoes
¼ tsp. salt
2 tbsp. grated cheese
pinch of fines herbes

Combine rice, onion, stock and oil in a small saucepan. Bring to a boil. Cover and simmer on low heat for 25 minutes.   Add remaining ingredients, except cheese. Simmer another 20 minutes or until rice is well cooked. Sprinkle cheese on top.

Suggestion for completing meal — hamburger patty and a glass of milk.

OMELETTE AUX FINES HERBES
Serves 1

2 eggs
½ tsp. snipped parsley
½ tsp. fresh chives

1 tsp. water
2 tsp. margarine
pinch of salt and pepper

Break the eggs into a small bowl and add parsley, chives, water, salt and pepper. Melt margarine in small (5 or 6 inch) frypan, preferably one with non-stick surface. Heat until a drop of water sizzles. At once add egg mixture and with spatula start loosening cooked sides and pushing towards centre. Tip pan so uncooked portion of egg runs underneath. Keep tipping and loosening until all surplus liquid is softly set. Fold in half and slide onto plate.

Suggestion for completing meal — whole wheat toast, salad and cheese in the omelette.

CHICKEN LIVER SUPREME
Serves 1

1 tbsp. vegetable oil
½ small onion, thinly-sliced
¼ lbs. chicken livers, sliced
pinch of salt and pepper

1 tsp. flour
¼ cup plain yogurt
¼ tsp. paprika

Heat oil in small frypan. Saute onion until partially cooked. Add sliced livers and cook over medium heat until cooked, about 5 to 10 minutes. Mix paprika with flour; sprinkle over livers. Stir to blend. Reduce heat and stir in yogurt and heat but do not boil.

Suggestion for completing meal — rice, green vegetable salad and a glass of milk.

Leftovers

Food cannot always be bought in just the exact amount that will be used at one meal, therefore, one cannot estimate the exact amount that will be eaten and occasionally there will be leftovers. Prevent food waste by saving leftovers. With a little imagination they can be turned into a number of tempting dishes.

When freezing leftovers wrap them tightly to keep food in good condition and save nutrients. Cool leftover foods quickly, and store, well-covered, in the refrigerator. Use within two to three days after cooking.

The smart cook plans for leftovers. They make meal preparation easier as the foods are already cooked. Leftovers can be the basis for many economical, time-saving meals. Some of the many dishes you can prepare using leftovers include soups, sandwiches (hot or cold), creamed and scalloped dishes, casseroles, main dish salads and puddings.

Leftover meat, fish and poultry

CHEF'S SALAD

Combine small pieces of leftover meat, fish or poultry with cheese cubes and chopped hard-boiled egg. Add to a mixed green salad of lettuce or spinach leaves, and grated carrot.

Suggestion for completing meal — whole wheat toast.

SHEPHERD'S PIE

180 C (350 F)
Serves 1

½ cup cooked beef cut in cubes
½ cup leftover vegetables
¼ cup liquid from vegetables, or water, or leftover gravy
salt
pepper
1 tbsp. finely chopped onions
½ cup mashed potatoes

In a casserole dish, combine beef cubes, vegetables, liquid, onions, salt and pepper to taste. Spread with layer of mashed potatoes. Top with a little grated cheese or margarine. Bake for 30 minutes.

Suggestion for completing meal — whole wheat roll and milk.

HOMEMADE SOUP FOR TWO

Serves 2

bones from any cooked meat or poultry
2 cups water
½ cup chopped vegetables (carrot or potato are good)
¼ cup uncooked rice, barley, noodles, or macaroni

Simmer bones in the water for one hour. Strain the broth to remove bones. Add to broth any meat left on the bones or left over from the meal. Stir in vegetables and rice, barley, noodles, or macaroni. Simmer 20 minutes or until vegetables and rice are tender. Season with salt and pepper to taste.

Suggestion for completing meal — whole wheat crackers and milk.

LEFTOVER CASSEROLE RECIPE

190 C (375 F)
Serves 1

Mix in a small casserole small pieces of leftover cooked or canned meat, fish, chicken or turkey. Add an equal amount of canned or cooked vegetables and also, if you like, cooked rice, macaroni or diced boiled potato. Mix well and moisten with one or more of the following: leftover gravy, condensed cream soup, milk, vegetable liquid, broth, meat stock or white sauce (p. 8). Season to taste.

Suggestion for completing meal — milk.

Leftover breads and cereals

RICE PUDDING

180 C (350 F)
Serves 1

½ cup cooked rice
1 egg slightly beaten
1 tbsp. sugar
pinch of salt
1 cup milk

Mix together rice, egg, sugar, salt and milk. Pour into small casserole or custard cups. Bake for 45 minutes. Serve warm or chilled. Variations: add nuts or raisins.

Suggestion for completing meal — tuna salad.

SOUR MILK MUFFINS

200 C (400 F)
Makes 6 muffins

1 cup enriched flour
2 tbsp. sugar
2 tsp. baking powder
¼ tsp. salt
1 egg
½ cup sour milk
1 tbsp. oil

Measure into bowl: flour, sugar, baking powder and salt. Add egg, sour milk and oil, stir lightly with a fork until moistened. Fill greased muffin or individual custard cups two-thirds full. Bake for 20-25 minutes or until top of muffins are brown. Makes 6 medium sized muffins.

Variations: If you have leftover cheese, add ½ cup grated cheese with dry ingredients. Crumbled bacon or raisins make a nice change too.

Suggestion for completing meal — poached egg, milk and orange juice.

PINEAPPLE FRENCH TOAST

Serves 1

1 egg
¼ cup pineapple juice (unsweetened)
dash of salt
2 slices bread
1 tbsp. margarine
2 slices unsweetened pineapple

Combine egg, pineapple juice and salt and mix until blended. Dip slices of bread into egg mixture (on both sides) and fry on medium heat in melted margarine until golden brown; turn and fry on opposite side. Serve topped with slices of pineapple.

Suggestion for completing meal — a glass of milk.

Leftover fruits and vegetables

POTATO SALAD
Serves 1

½ cup mashed or cubed cooked potato
1 hard-boiled egg, sliced
1 tbsp. yogurt or mayonnaise
salt and pepper

Mix together potato, egg slices and yogurt or mayonnaise. Season with salt and pepper.

Variations: add minced onion, celery, radish or grated cheese.

Suggestion for completing meal — grilled cheese sandwich and an apple.

VEGETABLE SALAD
Serves 1

Toss drained, canned or cooked leftover vegetables such as carrots, green beans, cauliflower or broccoli with enough salad dressing to moisten. Serve chilled on a lettuce cup.

Suggestion for completing meal — tuna cheese bun and milk.

MACARONI SALAD
Serves 1

½ cup cooked enriched macaroni
¼ cup leftover cooked meat (eg. chicken or beef)
¼ cup leftover cooked vegetables peas, green beans)
1 tbsp. diced celery (if desired)
1 tsp. minced onion (if desired)
1½ tbsp. mayonnaise
1/8 tsp. prepared mustard (optional)
pinch of salt
pinch of pepper

Combine macaroni, meat and vegetable in a bowl. Add celery and onion if desired. Mix together mayonnaise and prepared mustard. Add to bowl with salt and pepper and mix gently.

Suggestion for completing meal — a glass of milk.

Cooking With Herbs

Herbs are a delightful way to add an inexpensive gourmet touch to many dishes. They can be enjoyed either fresh or dried, and used in a variety of dishes to season meats, poultry, fish, eggs, vegetables, and fruit as well as salads, sauces, soups, and stuffings. Dried herbs offer a greater selection. Why not try to grow your own herbs such as chives, parsley, and thyme that you use frequently. You can buy the plants or seeds from most local stores. Information on how to grow them can be easily obtained by writing to either the Federal or Provincial Ministries of Agriculture. Herbs make lovely plants for the house and balcony and extra special gifts for your friends. If you decide to grow your own, here are a couple of ways that you can store your harvest:

1. Freezing: wash; drain; chop; freeze on trays; put into small bags; store in freezer.
2. Drying: wash; drain; spread on cheese cloth on a rack; cover with cheese cloth; dry 2 to 3 days in a warm dark place where there is good circulation; store in dark-coloured jars in a cool place.

The following are a few important tips on the use of fresh, frozen, and dried herbs:

1. Buy herbs in small quantities; they lose their flavour after a while.
2. Dried herbs should be crushed (rubbed between your hands) before using — it releases the flavor.
3. Add herbs to soups or stews in the last hour of cooking.
4. Don't thaw frozen herbs, put them directly into the dish you are preparing.
5. Store herbs in dark containers, preferably in a cool place — NOT above the stove.
6. The flavor of dried herbs is stronger than fresh; about 1 tsp. of crushed dried herbs equals 1 tbsp. of chopped fresh herbs.
7. Use herbs sparingly until you get familiar with the different flavors. Initially use about ¼ tsp. of crushed dried herbs per 4 servings — you can always add more.
8. Experiment with various herbs, but remember savory herbs should enhance the flavor of the dish, not overpower and disguise it.

Alphabetical index

	Page		Page
Cheese and Milk	6	Peking Tuna Salad	22
Apple Bread Pudding	10	Salmon French Toast	22
Basic Pudding Mix	8	Salmon Loaf	2
Chocolate	8	Saucy Fish and Peas	22
Coconut	8	Seafarer's Casserole	2
Pie Filling	9	Tuna Noodle Casserole	2
Vanilla	8	**Chicken**	2
Broccoli "Quiche"	10	Braised Chicken Livers	2
Broiled Super Sandwich	9	Chicken-Mushroom Casserole	2
Cheese Muffins	10	Chicken Rosemary	2
Cheese Sauce	8	Chicken Salad Supreme	2
Cheese Souffle	7	Chicken Soup	2
Cheese Straws	9	Oven-Stewed Chicken	2
Corn Chowder	11	Roasted or Baked Chicken	2
Cottage Stuffed Tomato	11	Simple Simon Chicken	2
Cream of Chicken Soup	9	Company Chicken Pie with biscuit topping	2
Macaroni and Cheese	7	**Whole Grain Cereals**	30
Welsh Rarebit	11	Apple Bran Muffins	3
White Sauce (basic)	8	Crusty Popovers	30
Yogurt, homemade	7	Dill Bread	3
Fruit and Vegetables	12	Drop Cheese Biscuits	3
Baked Apple	15	Four Week Bran Muffins	3
Baked Potato	13	Granola	3
Bert's Special Salad	15	Health Bread	3
Carrots in Casserole	14	Irish Bran Bread	34
Cinnamon Pears	14	Pancakes	3
Fresh Fruit Salad	13	Pancake Mix	32
Ginger Carrots	14	Skillet Bannock	3
Ratatouille	16	Three-Grain Biscuits	34
Saucy Vegetables	13	Vegetable Rice Pilaf	3
Stir-Fry Vegetables	16	Whole Wheat Soda Bread	30
Tangy Fruit Salad	15	**Ethnic Ideas**	37
Tropical Fruit Smoothie	15	Borscht	3
Vegetable Beef Casserole	16	Broccoli and Beef	3
Vegetable Protein	17	Cabbage Rolls	3
Baked Beans	19	Egg Foo Yong	40
Barley Vegetable Pilaf	20	Greek Salad	3
Lentil and Rice Casserole	19	Indian Curry	40
Savory Bean/Oat Patties	19	Len's Irish Chili	40
Split Pea Soup	18	Moussaka	3
Tomato Lentil Soup	20	**Desserts and Snacks**	41
Fish and Seafood	21	Apple Orange Toddy	4
Baked Fish with Herbs	22	Baked Cottage Cheese Custard	42
Breaded Fish Fillets	23	Custard Sauce (for topping fruit)	43
Crispy Fish Fillets	25	Fruit Crisp	42
Fish Foil Dinner	23	Fruit Whip	43
Hearty Fish Chowder	24		